The Maths Book: First Concepts

Over the past 60 years I have helped many children and young people between the ages of 4 and 20 with their mathematics. My aim always is to ensure children enjoy it, are challenged by it, never get bored, understand what they are doing, and grow to think mathematically.

When I reached the age of 81, my younger daughter presented me with a new grandson, Rufus. She asked me to write down some of the things I did with her when she was little, and with all the other children I have worked with since, so that she can do the same with Rufus.

So, to Tara, Rufus and all other parents and children who use this book: have fun and enjoy!

Text Copyright © Shirley Shaw

Grey Tiger Books 2018
GTB, 10–16 Ashwin Street, Dalston, London, E8 3DL
10 9 8 7 6 5 4 3 2 1

A catalogue record for this book is available from the British Library

Edited by Tara Cranswick
Illustrations by Fergal Stapleton
Design by Zoë Anspach
Printed by Latimer Trend & Company Ltd
ISBN 9781912107711

How to use this book

Answers are in orange

Activities to do together are marked with

Things to make are

■ ■ ■ means carry on with your own examples

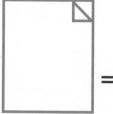 = notes to parents

Some Dos and Don'ts

- Don't tell your child you didn't like maths at school or that you couldn't do maths at school.

- It is possible to make mathematics fun! In this way you can give your child a love for mathematics.

- Help your child to "wake up" their mathematical brain. Mental arithmetic is very important for this.

- Repetition is important but if overdone it is just boring. When using repetition add a tune: songs are much easier to remember.

- You don't have to be sitting at a table for some of this work. You could be driving in the car, going for a walk or washing the dishes. Tara and I did a lot of mental work while she was in the bath.

- Try and correlate your work with that which your child is doing at school. If you start this after a few years at school, incorporate the early work to ensure their method is correct, and that they are understanding what they do.

- Mental work should be carried through to the teens: just ten quick questions off the cuff.

- What follows touches on each topic, but do practise and reinforce with your own examples.

- Think of this as fun brain-training. Thinking mathematically is not just about numbers or school, it is a skill for life.

- Mathematical connections have their own kind of magic, which can be discovered at any age, so I hope you all enjoy this book together.

Contents

Counting
to 10

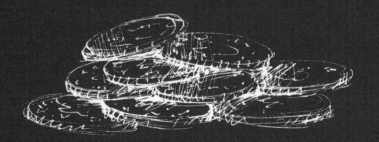

The first things we count should be objects: bottle tops, blocks, marbles, stars, raisins: the list is almost endless. Count slowly one by one so that the words 'one, two, three' start to mean something.

It is not wise to start with fingers because we cannot easily rid ourselves of them and we come to depend on them. I have seen children of 15 use their fingers to calculate simple sums: I was shocked. SO my advice is to avoid fingers altogether.

Far better is to have individual flash cards with 1,2,3...10 written on them and a piece of card with all the numbers 1...10.

Something like this

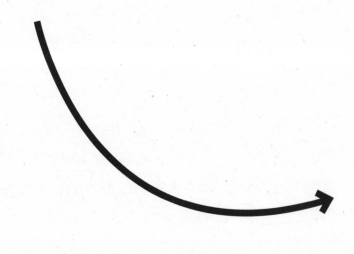

1

Something like this

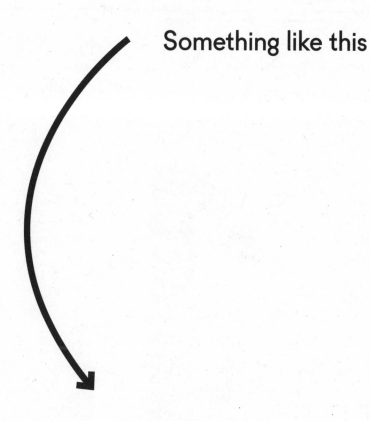

1 2 3 4 5

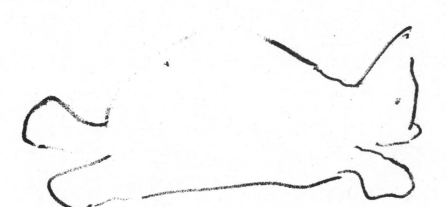

6   7   8   9   10

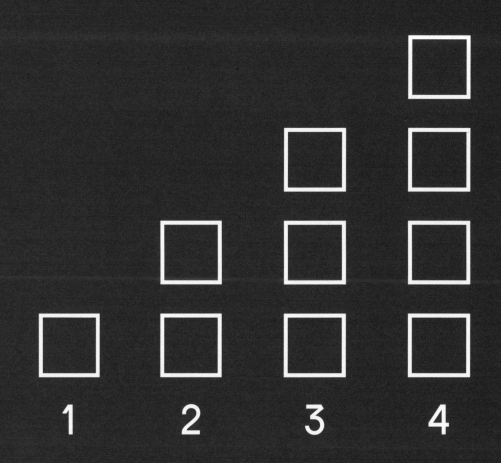

▶ Piling blocks

Cubic blocks (cubes) are useful as they can be placed one on top of each other. If you can, get a supply of 20 blocks.

The aim is to start to THINK mathematically.

Ask your child to give you 1 block. Put it aside.

Then ask for 2 more and place them beside the 1.

Then 3 and then 4. Place a number card next to each pile.

Now:

- Which pile is the biggest?

- Which pile is the smallest?

- Which pile is bigger, 1 or 2?

- Which pile is bigger, 2 or 4?

- Which is smaller, 1 or 2?

- Which is smaller, 1 or 3?

● ■ ■ ■

Start to play this game with any objects and with higher numbers. Compare different piles... Which are bigger? Which are smaller? In this way numbers start to become real in the world of things which surround us.

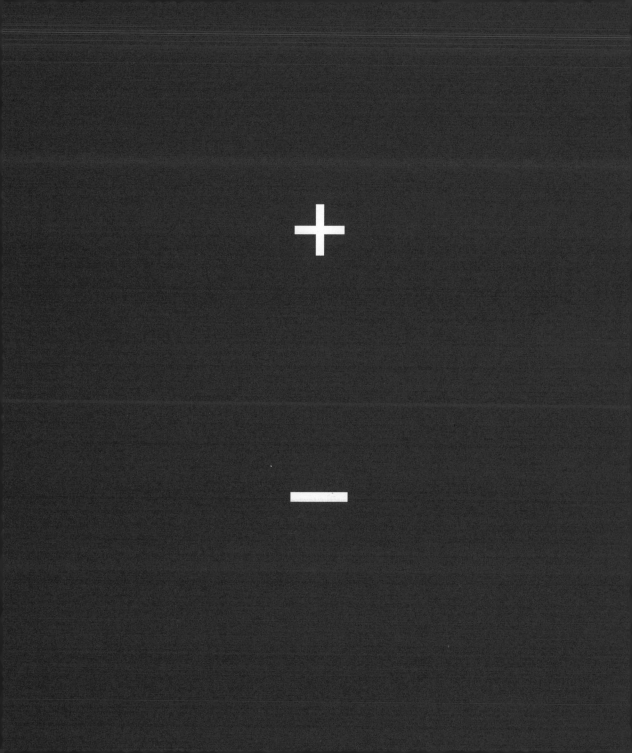

▶ Adding

Take 2 objects and put them down.
Ask your child for 5 more and put them with the 2.
How many are there all together? Count them...

7

So if you take 2 and add 5 you get 7.

In mathematics language this can be written as

$2 + 5 = 7$

Keep doing examples like this with different numbers (less than 10 for now) to give your child a sense of increasing and adding.

▶ Taking Away

Take 6 objects and put them down.

Ask your child to take 2 of them away.

So 6, take away 2, leaves? 4   Yes!

In mathematics language this is written:

$6 - 2 = 4$

Do a few more and ask how to write them and how to find the answers.

Then try the following:

$8 - 1 = \square$ $6 - 3 = \square$ $5 - 2 = \square$ $8 - 5 = \square$

$5 - 3 = \square$ $7 - 2 = \square$ $2 - 1 = \square$ $3 - 2 = \square$

Now mixed sums. Can you do them?

$2 + 5 =$ ☐ $7 - 3 =$ ☐ $6 + 1 =$ ☐ $9 - 1 =$ ☐

$5 + 2 =$ ☐ $5 - 1 =$ ☐ $5 + 4 =$ ☐ $5 - 4 =$ ☐

Make more examples for your child using either plus + or minus −.

Try to re-inforce the idea that + or "adding" is about getting bigger and increasing, and that − or "taking away" or "subtraction" is about getting smaller and decreasing.

Avoid fingers. Rather use blocks or objects.

Making a number chart: a "100 square"

Make a chart on A4 paper with 10 rows across and 10 columns down. Fill in the numbers 1....100. We have made a chart for you here which can be copied/photocopied and enlarged if you want.

Working with charts

- Point to 1 on your counting chart and ask your child to give you 1 block. Then ask them to find the flash card that corresponds to the chart and the block. Get them to say '1'. Encourage them to read '1' as well as understand the number.

- The next number is 2... 'Show me 2 blocks'....

- Then 3 ... and 4.

1	2	3	4	5	6	7	8	9	10
11	12	13	14	15	16	17	18	19	20
21	22	23	24	25	26	27	28	29	30
31	32	33	34	35	36	37	38	39	40
41	42	43	44	45	46	47	48	49	50
51	52	53	54	55	56	57	58	59	60
61	62	63	64	65	66	67	68	69	70
71	72	73	74	75	76	77	78	79	80
81	82	83	84	85	86	87	88	89	90
91	92	93	94	95	96	97	98	99	100

Hide 2 bottle tops in your hand and ask your child to guess how many you have. Show them. Were they right?

Do it again.

Now let them hide some and you guess how many there are.

March around the room together counting 1, 2, 3, 4 as you step.

When you feel you are both ready to go on to higher numbers, repeat the above with 5...6...7...8...9...10.

Making your 10 ladder

Using a ladder (real or paper) number the steps from 1 to 10. Climb them, counting the steps as you go.

- Ask your child to go to step 3. Are they higher or lower than step 7?

- Is step 5 higher or lower than step 2?

- Which is the highest: step 5,7, or 1?

Whilst playing try to incorporate the words 'more', 'more than', 'less', 'less than', 'the most', 'the least', 'the biggest', 'the smallest', ■ ■ ■

When they know their digits: 1,2,3,...10, find them on calendars, doors, clocks, books, anything really. This would also be a good time to introduce a pack of cards.

Bonds
of 10

What are bonds of 10?

2 numbers which add up to 10

Bonds are friends.

1 and 9

4 and 6

3 and 7

2 and 8

5 and 5

6 and 4

9 and 1

8 and 2

ACTIVITY

Take 1 stone and put it down.

Then take 9 stones and put them with the 1 stone.

Now count them. How many are there?
10 Yes!

These two numbers make 10, so they are friends and make a bond.

Now check with 4 and 6. Do they make 10?

Now let's find some more bonds.

Count out 7 marbles. If you take 1 more, does it make 10? Count them.
...no

Put the 1 marble back. Take 2 marbles and count them all. Do they make 10?
...no

So put those 2 back, and take 3 and count them all. Do they make 10?

Yes! So 7 and 3 are friends.

So now we have

1 and 9   4 and 6   7 and 3

We need to find a friend for 8 so check as above and find its friends. Do the same with 5.

So we have all our friends.

1 is friends with 9? Is 9 friends with 1?

4 and 6 are friends. Check if 6 and 4 are friends.

Then check 3 and 7, 2 and 8. These are all true friends as it has to go both ways.

1 and 9 ...

2 and 8...

3 and 7...

4 and 6...

5 and 5...

Write the numbers forwards and backwards:

1 2 3 4 5 6 7 8 9

9 8 7 6 5 4 3 2 1

And the friends come together!
All these pairs add up to make 10.

Remember, in mathematics language, we can write 'add' as +

and
'makes' as =

So to write 7 and 3 makes 10
we can write $7 + 3 = 10$

If $4 + \square = 10$ can you remember what to put in the box? Look at your friends.

Now what goes into these boxes?

Now don't forget your friends. Return to these bonds often. They are so important.

$5 + 5 = \boxed{}$

$1 + 9 = \boxed{}$

$6 + 4 = \boxed{}$

$2 + \boxed{} = 10$

$3 + \boxed{} = 10$

$4 + \boxed{} = 10$

$8 + 2 = \boxed{}$

$6 + \boxed{} = 10$

$5 + \boxed{} = 10$

$6 + 4 = \boxed{}$

$9 + 1 = \boxed{}$

$8 + \boxed{} = 10$

$9 + \boxed{} = 10$

$2 + 8 = \boxed{}$

$1 + \boxed{} = 10$

$7 + 3 = \boxed{}$

$3 + 7 = \boxed{}$

$7 + \boxed{} = 10$

Counting beyond 10

Using your number chart point to each number as you go, count up to 10 together.

Then count another 10 up to 20.

So 10 and another 10 gets you to 20.

So 10 + 10 = 20

And two 10s make 20

In mathematics language we can write this as:

2 x 10 = 20

When I first did this with my children I would call 20 'two-ty' to re-enforce the connection with 2. I later corrected it to 'twenty'. I did the same with 'three-ty' and 'five-ty' (the other numbers do it for you).

After 20, count another 10 and you get to 30.
So

$$10 + 10 + 10 = 30$$

And

$$3 \times 10 = 30$$

Do the same with 40, 50, 60, 70, 80, 90 and 100.

So

$$10 + 10 + 10 + 10 + 10 + 10 + 10 + 10 + 10 + 10 = 100$$

$$10 \times 10 = 100$$

Point out to your child that they can now add and multiply to 100. They should be very proud of themselves!

Re-enforce the number connection:

3 tens make 30
Now write it mathematically....... $3 \times 10 = 30$

7 tens make 70
Now write it mathematically.................... ?

Do a few more yourselves

Making your 30 ladder

Draw a ladder approximately 35cm high on fairly strong card.

Mark in even spaces all the numbers up to 30. Mark every tenth rung. These are '10' rungs: 10, 20, 30. Thicken these rungs or decorate them to make them look special.

Now draw 9 rungs between each of these big rungs.

Number all the rungs from 1 to…30.

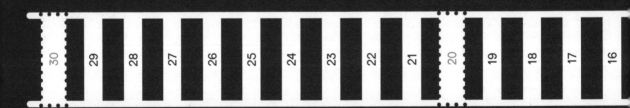

43

ACTIVITY

Count to 20 on both the number chart and the ladder.

Count to 30 on both the number chart and the ladder.

Note all the numbers from 10 to 20 start with 1.

Those from 20 to 30 start with 2.

Now count up your ladder in 10s to 30.

10, 20, 30

What is 10 steps or jumps more than 10?

What is 10 steps or jumps more than 20?

Make a ladder to 100 and keep working like this up the ladder.

1	2	3	4	5	6	7	8	9	10
11	12	13	14	15	16	17	18	19	20

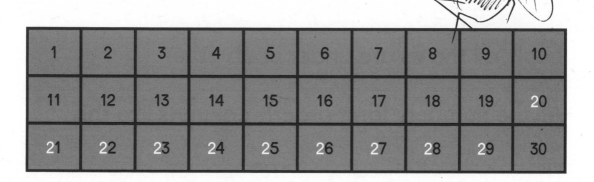

1	2	3	4	5	6	7	8	9	10
11	12	13	14	15	16	17	18	19	20
21	22	23	24	25	26	27	28	29	30

45

▶ Looking at your number chart

Count to 20.

Count in 10s down the 10 column to 100.

Count these backwards, clapping as you finish.
Count from 10 backwards, ending with 'Blast off'.

Now look at 40 on the chart.

What is the next number going across? 41
And the next, and the next, and so on until 50.
Then? ...51 And so on up to 60, 70, 80, 90, 100.

Look: all the 1s are under each other
Look: all the 6s are under each other

All the numbers form orderly columns like this.

Now count all the way to 100 on your chart.

► **Now look at rows**

Look at the first row on your number chart.
Now look at the third row. What do you notice?
How are they different? How are they similar?

The numbers in the third row all start with 2 so
they are all 20s 'two-ties' and this row ends with
30 'three-ty'.

So the next row starts with 3.

Look at the row starting with 6. What do we call
these? 60s 'sixties'. And the last number is 70 so
the next row starts with 7

How many numbers are there in the 1st row? 2nd
row? 9th row?

■ ■ ■

- Find the column that starts with 10, and count down the column: 10, 20, 30 ... 100

- Now count up the column from 100.

- Colour the column with a 3 at the top 3, 13, 23... 93. These all end in 3.

- Colour the column in which the numbers all end in 7.

- Now colour 48, and count on 10 more places. Where do you get to? 58 And then another. 10 more places. Where do you get to? 68 And another and another.

- What do you think you must add to 28 to make 38? If you are not sure, count it out.

- How many do you need to add to 25 to make 35?

- And 43 to make 53?

- If you add 10 to 37 what will you get? Count it out if necessary.

Play with these ■ ■ ■

Do more like this now, and in the next few days. Then complete these sums:

10 + 10 = ☐   23 + 10 = ☐
20 + 10 = ☐   49 + 10 = ☐
30 + 10 = ☐   71 + 10 = ☐

What big sums they can do just from counting!

Keep making up more examples for your child.

ACTIVITY

Now take your big ladder.
Count up the steps in tens.
Can you find 10, 20, 50, 80 ...

Now find random numbers: 23, 45, 67... etc.
Move around the ladder like you did with your
number chart until you feel you know it.

▶ Marbles or stones

Revise your bonds of 10:

1 + ☐ = 10   2 + ☐ = 10   3 + ☐ = 10

4 + ☐ = 10   5 + ☐ = 10   6 + ☐ = 10

7 + ☐ = 10   8 + ☐ = 10   9 + ☐ = 10

If you have 3 marbles, how many more will you need to make 10?

If you have 5 marbles, how many more will you need to make 10?

Do this with all of the bonds.   ■ ■ ■

If you play Monopoly, it can reinforce the 10s:

- There are ten spaces on each side.
- Use the board to count in 10s
- If you sit on 'GO', and throw 7 will you reach jail? No
- Move seven spaces. How many spaces are left till the end of the row? 3 ..because 7 + 3 = 10
- You're sitting on Chance (7). Now throw again. If you get 6... how many spaces to jail? 3
- Move 6: 3 to jail and 3 after jail (3 + 3 = 6)
- Start from GO again. You throw 14. Is that more or less than 10? How many more? 4 So jump straight to jail and then count 4 from there.

Play around the board using the four corners as your "tens" and asking how many less than or more than.

Remember the tedium of being forced to learn your times tables?

Rote learning should not be a part of mathematics.

In my experience, this is one of the points at which education can fail our children, where they lose the sense and meaning of what they are doing.

If you can give them an understanding of numbers, and the magic of multiplication, this can form the basis of a true enjoyment of mathematics...and even tables.

10x table

Children discover the logic of this table with their number chart and ladder.

Re-enforce by asking questions in any order:

5 x 10 = ?   9 x 10 = ?   2 x 10 = ?   ■ ■ ■

Now we want them to think about the multiplication process in reverse. They have done 3 x 10 = 30. Now ask them: how many 10s in 30? Answer: 3

Continue through the table in random order. You will notice that these are actually the beginnings of understanding division, but don't use that word yet. With any luck they will understand the process before they learn the word.

$$1 \times 10 = 10$$
$$2 \times 10 = 20$$
$$3 \times 10 = 30$$
$$4 \times 10 = 40$$
$$5 \times 10 = 50$$
$$6 \times 10 = 60$$
$$7 \times 10 = 70$$
$$8 \times 10 = 80$$
$$9 \times 10 = 90$$
$$10 \times 10 = 100$$
$$11 \times 10 = 110$$
$$12 \times 10 = 120$$

Bridging through 10

If your child has been adding numbers greater than 10 for some time, give them an example: 8 + 5 and ask them to show you how they work it out.

There is no wrong way, and in my time as a teacher I have been amazed at the ingenuity of children to create their own way through mathematical problems.

However, to make the years ahead much easier I would like you to guide them to use the following method. Guide and re-enforce this method until your child does this automatically.

Remember: fingers are not a good tool.

You can use your ladders to help in the beginning.

7 + 5

- First ask how much you must add to 7 to make 10. 3

- If we use 3 to get to 10. How many of the 5 are left over? 2

- 10 + 2 = 12

- Therefore:

$$7 + 5 = 12$$

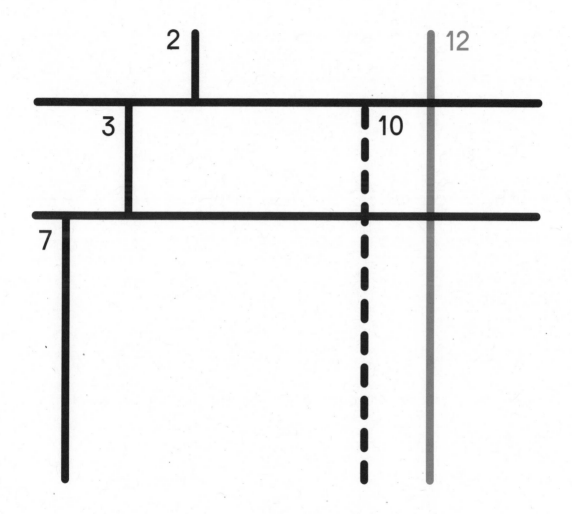

59

8 + 7

- In your head start with 8.

- How many more to 10? 2

- Move up 2 to 10. So how many are left from 7?

- 7 − 2 = 5

- Now from 10 move up 5 and your answer is? 15

- Therefore:

$$8 + 7 = 15$$

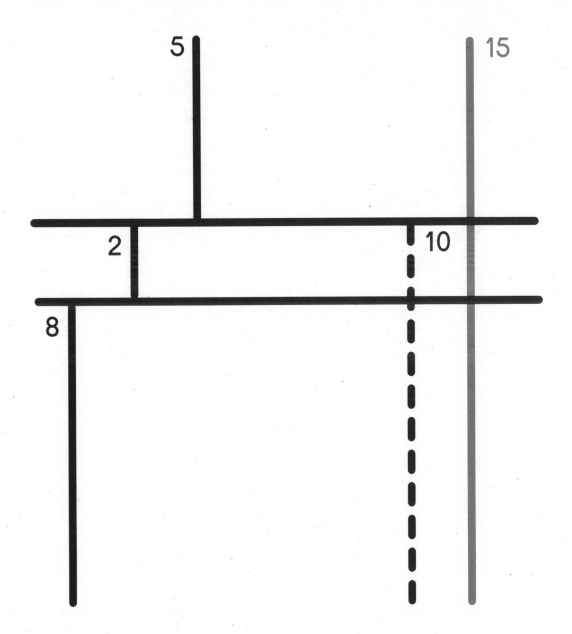

61

9 + 4
· · · · ·

- Start with 9.

- How many more do you need to make 10? 1

- 1 from 4 leaves? 3

- 10 + 3 = 13

- Therefore:

$$9 + 4 = 13$$

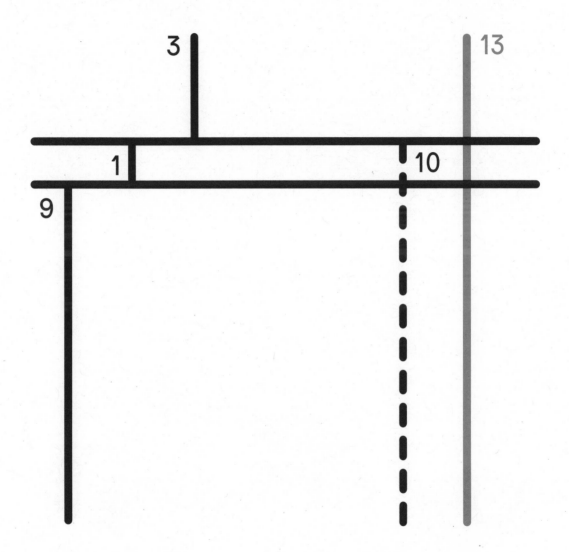

Notice how all of the above move around 10.

This is working with previous knowledge of adding to 10 and using the bonds of 10 (TRUE FRIENDS).

Do a lot of these together.

Remember 10 must be your stepping stone.

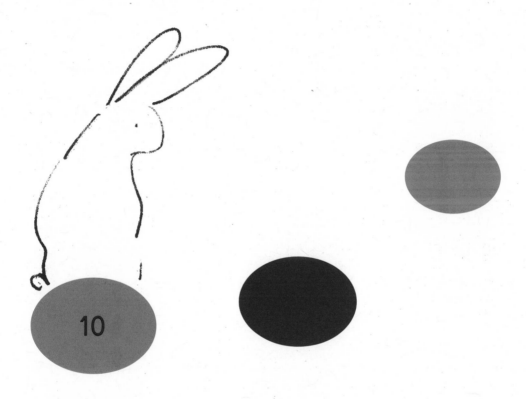

10

Now let's try some bigger ones...

17 + 5

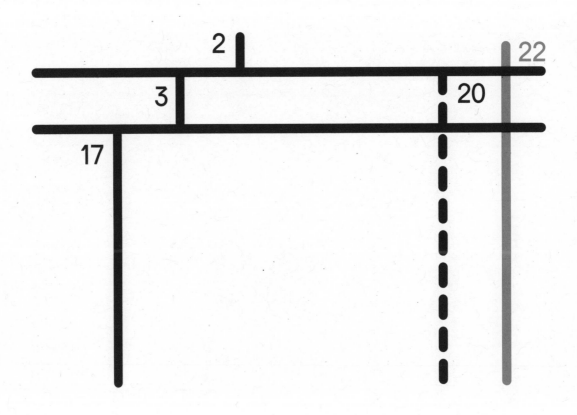

17 + 5 = 22

27 + 5

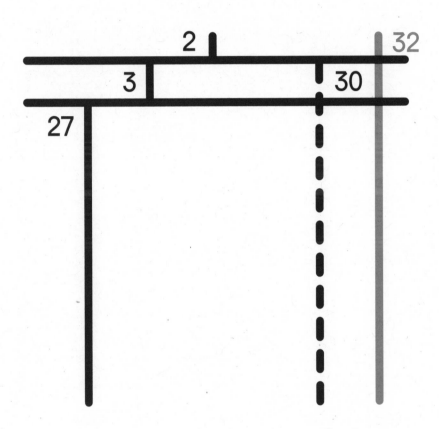

27 + 5 = 32

97 + 5

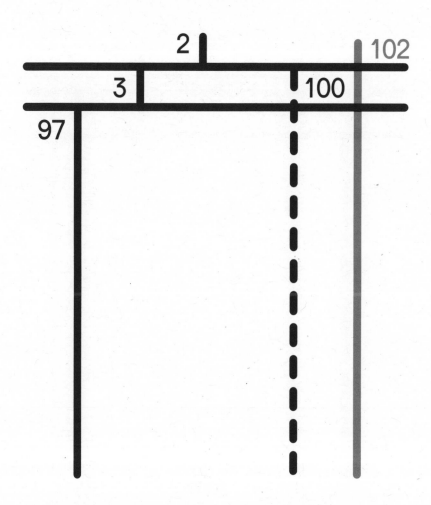

97 + 5 = 102

997 + 5

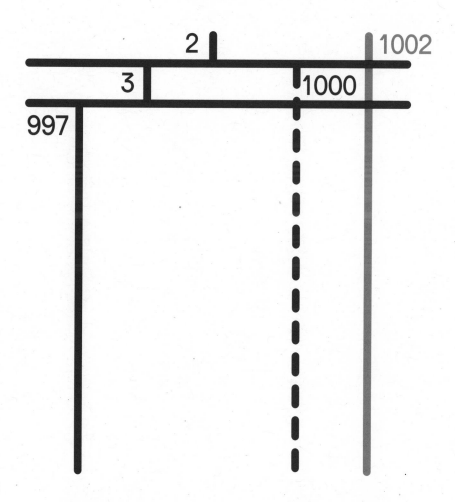

997 + 5 = 1002

Children are always so impressed that they can count around 100 and 1000... Point out how big these numbers are and how well they must be learning to count around them.

Counting on

on

an
important
concept

Start to use your number chart to count on.
Point to 23 and count on from there (24, 25, - -).
This is easy and needs to be done every day
in order to pick up this habit. Start from a few
different numbers. Count together at first but
then let your child count alone.

This habit of counting on helps with adding. For
example, if asked to add 23 and 3, you don't have
to start with 1, 2, 3, 4, - - - 23, 24, 25, 26. You can
be confident to start with 23 and count 3 more.

Also count backwards together.

Always throw in a backwards countdown from 10.

10, 9, 8, 7, 6, 5, 4, 3, 2, 1 ... BLAST OFF.

Practise this with a chart and without a chart.

The Game

The aim of this game is to become familiar with numbers and their order. It should always be readily available so that your child and their friends can use it at any time.

Make 2 more number charts for the game.

Make them quite large and out of cardboard so you can re-use them often.

Cut 1 number chart into separate numbers: 1...100.

Place these onto a tray on a low table. Place the second chart next to the tray full of numbers.

Nothing else should be on the table.

▶ How to Play

Each child plays individually but together with others around. A child will take a number from the tray, turn it the right way round, read it aloud, find the same number on the number chart and place their number on top of it. Then repeat.

The aim is for children to recognise numbers and become familiar with their position on the number chart.

I have seen this game in a classroom. When children had finished their work they would run to it eager to play.

5x table

The 5 times table has such a definite pattern that it is actually very easy to remember.

We have written it down here for you to look at, but more importantly start to get a real feeling for it with the activities which follow.

Once you have done a few of these, look back at the table and point out the repetition of the 10s and 5s.

$$1 \times 5 = 5$$
$$2 \times 5 = 10$$
$$3 \times 5 = 15$$
$$4 \times 5 = 20$$
$$5 \times 5 = 25$$
$$6 \times 5 = 30$$
$$7 \times 5 = 35$$
$$8 \times 5 = 40$$
$$9 \times 5 = 45$$
$$10 \times 5 = 50$$
$$11 \times 5 = 55$$
$$12 \times 5 = 60$$

▶ Colouring and chanting

On a new number chart make a pattern for 5:
Count 1, 2, 3, 4, colour 5. Count another five: 6,
7, 8, 9, colour 10. Count 11, 12, 13, 14, colour 15
and so on until you see the pattern develop.
Colour the pattern right up to 50 .
Together count the coloured numbers
5, 10, 15, 20, 25, 30, 35, 40, 45, 50

Read the coloured numbers again and again,
turning it into a song. Try doing it with eyes closed.

These are important numbers because they are
multiples of 5. Your child won't really understand
this yet but this way of working develops an
intrinsic feel for the numbers.

Small children love the sing-song of the 5, 10, 15
and feel important when they do it. However, you
must now make sure they know what it all means.

▶ Coins

Collect at least twenty 5p coins. Most children will be familiar with these.

• Give your child 1 coin and ask the value.
Ask how many pence make up this coin.
Give another coin and ask how much these 2 are together. Help to count it out if necessary. 5, 10
Add another coin. Now how many?
Add another coin. Now how many?
So counting, coin by coin to 50 ...

• Now take them all together and start counting in 5s: 5, 10, 15, 20, 25...

• Now give 2 coins. How much is that worth?
10.... so 5 + 5 = 10
Now give 3 coins. How much is that worth?
15 ......so 5 + 5 + 5 = 15
Continue in this way up to 100.

• Now ask for 35p

Get them to count out, 5, 10, 15... 35

Now ask how many coins make 35 pence...Count them 7

HOLD ON – you just did multiplication!!

5 x 7 = 35

Let's write down the 5 times table in the old-fashioned way:

1 x 5 = ☐   6 x 5 = ☐

2 x 5 = ☐   7 x 5 = ☐

3 x 5 = ☐   8 x 5 = ☐

4 x 5 = ☐   9 x 5 = ☐

5 x 5 = ☐   10 x 5 = ☐

If this is too difficult start with 1p coins.

Now together fill in the answers using the coins.

▶ Reversing

Now let's do multiplication in reverse:
How many 5s in 10? Answer: 2
How many 5s in 50? Answer: 10
Etc. in random order.

Don't use the word "divide" yet, but keep up with these exercises.

Remember you can do these any time, any place.

2x table

Never think of trying to
memorise these tables,
let them just be there.
Use them like you use your
charts and ladders. Refer
to them for answers or
to re-enforce the ideas
introduced by the coins.

$$1 \times 2 = 2$$
$$2 \times 2 = 4$$
$$3 \times 2 = 6$$
$$4 \times 2 = 8$$
$$5 \times 2 = 10$$
$$6 \times 2 = 12$$
$$7 \times 2 = 14$$
$$8 \times 2 = 16$$
$$9 \times 2 = 18$$
$$10 \times 2 = 20$$
$$11 \times 2 = 22$$
$$12 \times 2 = 24$$

On a new number chart make a pattern for 2:
Count 1, colour 2; count 3, colour 4; count 5,
colour 6 and so on until you see the pattern.
Colour the pattern right up to 50.
Together count the coloured numbers
2, 4, 6, 8, 10, 12, 14, 16, 18, 20, 22...50
These are called even numbers.

Turn this into a song. Now march around the
room or your garden. Whisper 1, shout 2, whisper
3, shout 4 ▪ ▪ ▪

1	2	3	4	5	6	7	8	9	10
11	12	13	14	15	16	17	18	19	20
21	22	23	24	25	26	27	28	29	30
31	32	33	34	35	36	37	38	39	40
41	42	43	44	45	46	47	48	49	50

▶ Counting objects

Find something to count: bottle tops, marbles, blocks, stones, while driving you can count cars.

- First count in 2s then check by counting in 1s.
- Do this with lots of different objects.

Now go back to your chart.
Look at the first coloured column on your number chart: what do you notice?
They all end in 2: hint a bit if necessary.

- Now count down this column:
  2, 12, 22, 32, 42
- What does the next coloured column end in?
  4
- Now count down the column:
  4, 14, 24, 34, 44
- Now find the columns where all the numbers end in 6s, now in 8s.

▶ Calculations

- Use a counting tool (objects) if necessary.

- Find the answers to:

$1 + 1 =$ ☐ –> How many 1s? 2 –> So 1 x 2 = 2

$2 + 2 =$ ☐ –> How many 2s? 2 –> So 2 x 2 = 4

$3 + 3 =$ ☐ --->

$4 + 4 =$ ☐ --->

$5 + 5 =$ ☐ --->

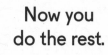

Now you
do the rest.

Next: try just with 2s:

$2 + 2 =$ ☐

$2 + 2 + 2 =$ ☐

$2 + 2 + 2 + 2 =$ ☐

$2 + 2 + 2 + 2 + 2 =$ ☐

So ②+② = 4, and two 2s = 4
You can write this mathematically: $2 \times 2 = 4$

Repeat this with three 2s, four 2s and five 2s

②+②+② = 6   so $2 \times 3 = 6$
                               or $3 \times 2 = 6$

■   ■   ■

ACTIVITY

Now fill in the answers here:

1 x 2   =   ☐   6 x 2   =   ☐

2 x 2   =   ☐   7 x 2   =   ☐

3 x 2   =   ☐   8 x 2   =   ☐

4 x 2   =   ☐   9 x 2   =   ☐

5 x 2   =   ☐   10 x 2   =   ☐

10 x 2 = 20, so... 10 + 10 = 20, so... double 10 = 20

3 x 2 = 6, so... 3 + 3 = 6, so... double 3 = 6

11 x 2 = 22, so... 11 + 11 = 22, so... double 11 = 22

Re-enforce how these three things go together.

Now let's do reverse multiplication.

How many 2s in 10?   5
What is half of 10?   5

If 2 x 5 = 10, how many 2s in 10?
              how many 5s in 10?
What is half of 10?

If 2 x 10 = 20, how many 2s in 20?
What is half of 20?

■ ■ ■

Doubling

Doubling is a very important part of mathematical thinking. Children enjoy the challenge and it also helps them with their tables.

Doubling means 2 x

So double 3 is 2 x 3 or 3 + 3

Double 1 = ☐   Double 300 = ☐

Double 2 = ☐   Double 4 = ☐

Double 3 = ☐   Double 40 = ☐

Double 100 = ☐   Double 400 = ☐

Double 200 = ☐

Offer a challenge:

Double 1. Now double the answer, then double that answer... and so on 2, 4, 8, 16, 32, 64...

See how far they can go, and then let them work out some of the answers on their own.
Double like this often and let them go as high as possible, getting further each time.

Now try:

Double 2
Double 20

Double 4
Double 40

Double 5
Double 50

Now double 20 and double 3... so what will be double 23?
That was more difficult, wasn't it?
Practise some of these.

Double 42 < Double 40 } = ☐
            Double 2

Double 34 < Double 30 } = ☐
            Double 4

Double 66 < Double 60 } = ☐
            Double 6

Double 2 is.. 4

AND

Double the 2x table is .... the 4x table

$2 \times 2 = 4$ So $4 \times 2 = 8$

Double

$2 \times 5 = 10$ So $4 \times 5 =$

Double

$2 \times 7 = 14$ So $4 \times 7 =$

Double

What is double 4? 8

AND

Double the 4x table is .... the 8x table.

$4 \times 3 = \text{(12)}$ So $8 \times 3 = \text{(24)}$

Double

$4 \times 5 = \text{(20)}$ So $8 \times 5 =$ ⟲

Double

$4 \times 9 = \text{(36)}$ So $8 \times 9 =$ ⟲

Double

Now fill in the answers below:

	Double	Double again
1 x 2 = ☐	1 x 4 = ☐	1 x 8 = ☐
2 x 2 = ☐	2 x 4 = ☐	2 x 8 = ☐
3 x 2 = ☐	3 x 4 = ☐	3 x 8 = ☐
4 x 2 = ☐	4 x 4 = ☐	4 x 8 = ☐
5 x 2 = ☐	5 x 4 = ☐	5 x 8 = ☐
6 x 2 = ☐	6 x 4 = ☐	6 x 8 = ☐
7 x 2 = ☐	7 x 4 = ☐	7 x 8 = ☐
8 x 2 = ☐	8 x 4 = ☐	8 x 8 = ☐
9 x 2 = ☐	9 x 4 = ☐	9 x 8 = ☐
10 x 2 = ☐	10 x 4 = ☐	10 x 8 = ☐
11 x 2 = ☐	11 x 4 = ☐	11 x 8 = ☐
12 x 2 = ☐	12 x 4 = ☐	12 x 8 = ☐

So if you are asked for 6 x 8
Think: 6 x 2 = 12
Double that is 6 x 4 = 24
Double that is 6 x 8 = 48

Now work out 3 x 8, 7 x 8,   ■ ■ ■
NO ROTE LEARNING – JUST THINKING

By knowing the 2x table and being able to
double, you can do the 4x and the 8x tables!

Do these often
and randomly,
for example
7 x 8...
7 x 2 double
7 x 4 double
so 7 x 8 = ?

4x table

$$1 \times 4 = 4$$
$$2 \times 4 = 8$$
$$3 \times 4 = 12$$
$$4 \times 4 = 16$$
$$5 \times 4 = 20$$
$$6 \times 4 = 24$$
$$7 \times 4 = 28$$
$$8 \times 4 = 32$$
$$9 \times 4 = 36$$
$$10 \times 4 = 40$$
$$11 \times 4 = 44$$
$$12 \times 4 = 48$$

8x table

1   x 8 = 8
2   x 8 = 16
3   x 8 = 24
4   x 8 = 32
5   x 8 = 40
6   x 8 = 48
7   x 8 = 56
8   x 8 = 64
9   x 8 = 72
10 x 8 = 80
11 x 8 = 88
12 x 8 = 96

Halving

Now we want to introduce halving as the opposite of doubling.

Keep up the doubling we learnt. It is a good mental exercise.

Remember, it went like this: start with 1... double it, double the answer, double again.... See how far you can go, hoping you'll get further each time you try.

Children like big numbers. It makes them feel important, so introduce the 100s, 1000s and even millions.

▶ Halving

Cut an apple in half to demonstrate what a half is and that 2 halves make 1.

Now take 10 grapes and share them with each other. One for you and one for me, until they are finished. Let your child count how many you have, and how many they have.

SO .... ½ of 10 is 5.

Also, double 5 is 10.

Now let your child share 8 objects between the two of you. How many do you each have? 4
So half of 8 is 4.

Also 4 + 4 = 8 or ½ of 8 = 4 or double 4 = 8
Play with these, connecting the halving and doubling.

Then start with 20 ----   Half of 20 is? 10
                           Half of 10 is? 5

Now double 5. Double that, and double that, and double that 80

Now halve 40, halve 20, and halve 10 5

Now try with examples from the 2x table:
Half of 2?
          Half of 6?
          Half of 14?

Take it to your child's level and keep this up.

3x table

$1 \times 3 = 3$

$2 \times 3 = 6$

$3 \times 3 = 9$

$4 \times 3 = 12$

$5 \times 3 = 15$

$6 \times 3 = 18$

$7 \times 3 = 21$

$8 \times 3 = 24$

$9 \times 3 = 27$

$10 \times 3 = 30$

$11 \times 3 = 33$

$12 \times 3 = 36$

▶ Counting and Chanting

On your number chart colour in every 3ʳᵈ number.
Count 1, 2, then colour 3.
Do this again and again until you get to 30.

Does it make a pattern?

Do you want to complete the pattern?
Now do a bit of marching and chanting just for good measure!

We did this for the 5x and 2x tables before.

Practise the 3x table for a few days. Because we can double we can also do the 6x and 12x tables.

		Double		**Double again**	
1 x 3	= 3	1 x 6	= □	1 x 12	= □
2 x 3	= 6	2 x 6	= □	2 x 12	= □
3 x 3	= 9	3 x 6	= □	3 x 12	= □
4 x 3	= 12	4 x 6	= □	4 x 12	= □
5 x 3	= □	5 x 6	= □	5 x 12	= □
6 x 3	= □	6 x 6	= □	6 x 12	= □
7 x 3	= □	7 x 6	= □	7 x 12	= □
8 x 3	= □	8 x 6	= □	8 x 12	= □
9 x 3	= □	9 x 6	= □	9 x 12	= □
10 x 3	= □	10 x 6	= □	10 x 12	= □
11 x 3	= □	11 x 6	= □	11 x 12	= □
12 x 3	= □	12 x 6	= □	12 x 12	= □

How many 6s in 12? How many 6s in 18?

How many 12s in 24? How many 12s in 48?

■ ■ ■

6x table

1   x 6 = 6
2   x 6 = 12
3   x 6 = 18
4   x 6 = 24
5   x 6 = 30
6   x 6 = 36
7   x 6 = 42
8   x 6 = 48
9   x 6 = 54
10 x 6 = 60
11 x 6 = 66
12   x 6 = 72

12x table

1   x 12 = 12
2   x 12 = 24
3   x 12 = 36
4   x 12 = 48
5   x 12 = 60
6   x 12 = 72
7   x 12 = 84
8   x 12 = 96
9   x 12 = 108
10 x 12 = 120
11 x 12 = 132
12 x 12 = 144

Another look at tables

Now let's see where we are with our tables...

You already know:
your 5x and 10x tables
your 2x, 4x and 8x tables
your 3x, 6x and 12x tables

So that leaves the 7x table, 9x table and 11x table.

11x table is an easy one!
You already know:

2 x 11 = ☐

3 x 11 = ☐

4 x 11 = ☐

5 x 11 = ☐

6 x 11 = ☐

8 x 11 = ☐

10 x 11 = ☐

Can you see the pattern?
So what is...

7 x 11 = ☐

9 x 11 = ☐

And what about after 10?

Well, there is a trick for 11 x big numbers...

11 x 18

1   1
       +
       8
       =
1   9   8

= 198

11 x 52

5   5
       +
       2
       =
5   7   2

= 572

11 x 23

2   2
       +
       3
       =
2   5   3

= 253

Can you see how to do it? Let's try some more:

11 x 43
= 4 7 3

11 x 36
= 3 9 6

11 x 72
= 7 9 2

Now can you do these:

11 x 17 = ☐

11 x 25 = ☐

11 x 41 = ☐

11 x 34 = ☐

11 x 63 = ☐

11 x 81 = ☐

NB: The sum of the two digits must not be more than 9 for this trick (at this age) i.e. not 11 x 83 because 8 + 3 is greater than 9.

Repeat this often.

This is such a quick way to do the 11x table with no fingers and no paper.

11x table

1   x 11 = 11
2   x 11 = 22
3   x 11 = 33
4   x 11 = 44
5   x 11 = 55
6   x 11 = 66
7   x 11 = 77
8   x 11 = 88
9   x 11 = 99
10 x 11 = 110
11 x 11 = 121
12 x 11 = 132

9x table

The 9 times table is my favourite as there are all sorts of patterns.

Practise 20 − 2, 70 − 7, 90 − 9, 50 − 5, 10 − 1, etc. together. When your child has mastered this, show them the easiest way to do the 9x table.

1 x 9 = [10 − 1] = 9
2 x 9 = [20 − 2] = 18
3 x 9 = [30 − 3] = 27
4 x 9 = [40 − 4] = 36
5 x 9 = [50 − 5] = 45
6 x 9 = [60 − 6] = 54
7 x 9 = [70 − 7] = 63
8 x 9 = [80 − 8] = 72
9 x 9 = [90 − 9] = 81

Can you see the pattern?

$$1 \times 9 = 9$$
$$2 \times 9 = 18$$
$$3 \times 9 = 27$$
$$4 \times 9 = 36$$
$$5 \times 9 = 45$$
$$6 \times 9 = 54$$
$$7 \times 9 = 63$$
$$8 \times 9 = 72$$
$$9 \times 9 = 81$$
$$10 \times 9 = 90$$
$$11 \times 9 = 99$$
$$12 \times 9 = 108$$

Here is another great pattern to look at together.

Write 0 – 9 vertically down and 0 – 9 up in columns.

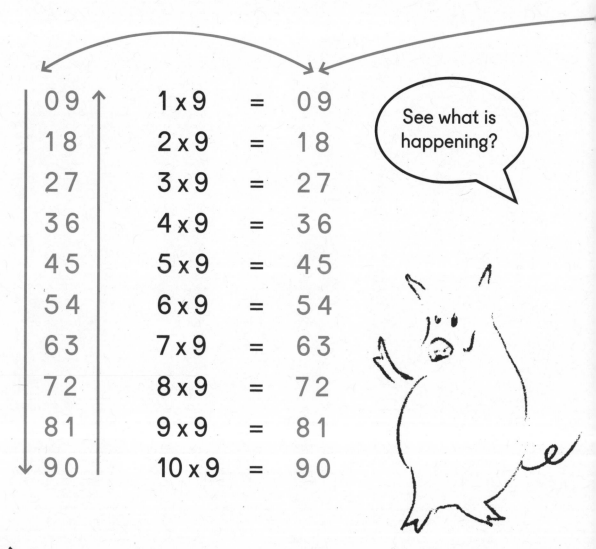

09	1 x 9	=	09
18	2 x 9	=	18
27	3 x 9	=	27
36	4 x 9	=	36
45	5 x 9	=	45
54	6 x 9	=	54
63	7 x 9	=	63
72	8 x 9	=	72
81	9 x 9	=	81
90	10 x 9	=	90

See what is happening?

Now take these columns and add them up:

Another bit of 9x magic!

0 + 9 = ☐
1 + 8 = ☐
2 + 7 = ☐
3 + 6 = ☐
4 + 5 = ☐
5 + 4 = ☐
6 + 3 = ☐
7 + 2 = ☐
8 + 1 = ☐
9 + 0 = ☐

7x table

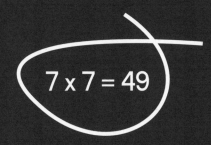

7 x 7 = 49

This is the only sum in the 7x table that you don't already know from learning the other tables. WOW!

Don't forget it.

$$1 \times 7 = 7$$
$$2 \times 7 = 14$$
$$3 \times 7 = 21$$
$$4 \times 7 = 28$$
$$5 \times 7 = 35$$
$$6 \times 7 = 42$$
$$7 \times 7 = 49$$
$$8 \times 7 = 56$$
$$9 \times 7 = 63$$
$$10 \times 7 = 70$$
$$11 \times 7 = 77$$
$$12 \times 7 = 84$$

100 –

This is a good game for the bath.

First revise the 10 bonds, 10 – 3, 10 – 5?
8 and what makes 10?
7 and what makes 10?

$2 + \square = 10$

$9 + \square = 10$

Next take it to the 10s
80 and what makes 100?
70 and what makes 100?

$20 + \square = 100$

$90 + \square = 100$

Now introduce the 100 – game.

100 − 24 = ?

Start at 24, counting up, which 10 comes first?
30

How many to get from 24 to 30?
6

100 − 30 = 70

70 + 6 = 76

So

100 − 24 = 76

Once again you are reaching to the next 10.

100 − 57 = ?

57 goes up to? 60

How many steps from 57 to 60? 3

100 − 60 = 40
And the extra 3 makes 43

100 − 57 = 43

Take it slowly at first. Once your child gets it, they will enjoy the challenge of this game.

Scribble space

Dear Readers, I hope that this book helps you and your children to see maths in a new way. I have played these games and exercises with all the children I have taught, and with my own children and grandchildren through the years, and I hope they will be just as useful to you.

Please make sure to keep up the mental arithmetic throughout their school careers, and continue to make the exercises more and more challenging as your child progresses. But remember: keep maths fun.

"...mathematics is, in its way, the poetry of logical ideas." Albert Einstein